The 20-Minute

Bible
Study
Workbook

The 20-Minute
Bible
Study
Workbook

Volume 1 – 13 Weeks

John, Romans, Ruth, Exodus 1-24, Hebrews

J. A. Marucci
R. K. Brownrigg

Happy Tent Media Group

INTRODUCTION

This Bible study workbook has been carefully designed and refined over many years to help you effectively learn what the Bible says. The workbook is set up for Monday through Saturday use, and a day's reading and answering questions will usually take about 20 minutes. It is primarily designed for personal study but can be adapted for small group use.

Try to set aside the same time each day. If you are a morning person, try to do this first thing. Not everyone is a morning person, and many people prefer later in the day, evening, or during a lunch break. Whenever the best time of day is for you, try to set aside the same time daily.

To get the most out of this workbook, you will want to read the daily assigned reading and write down your answers to the questions presented. You can write in the workbook, as there is space under each question to write down answers.

It is normal to miss a time or two for various reasons. Don't let missing discourage you from picking it back up. If you miss a day or even a week, start again with the next day's reading or the beginning of the following week.

Finally, your positive rating and a written review of this workbook will make it more readily available for others to find and use. If you find this workbook helpful, please consider taking a moment and posting a review on Amazon.com.

Thank you, and God bless you as you study the Bible!

J. A. Marucci
R. K. Brownrigg

Name:_____ Date Started: _____

Weekly Checklist/Contents:

"...be attentive to my words; incline your ear to my sayings. Let them not escape from your sight; keep them within your heart. For they are life to those who find them, and healing to all their flesh." — Proverbs 4:20-22 (ESV)

Week 1 — This week's Bible reading will begin our walk through the Gospel of John. We will look at Jesus the revealed Son of God, John the Baptist's testimony of Jesus, Jesus' first miracle, Jesus and Nicodemus, and Jesus and the woman at the well.

Monday

Read John 1:1–18

What do we learn about Jesus in the opening verses of this gospel? (John 1:1–4)

What else are we told about Jesus? What are we told about those who received Him and believed in His name? (John 1:10–14)

What did John the Baptist say concerning Jesus? What other things are revealed to us in these verses? (John 1:15–18)

Read John 1:19–34

Who did John the Baptist say he was and was not when asked? What was his mission? (John 1:19–23)

What did John the Baptist say when he saw Jesus coming to him? What are we told as to the reason for John's ministry to baptize people? (John 1:29–31)

What else did John say concerning Jesus? (John 1:32–34)

Read John 1:35–51

How did Jesus call His first two disciples? What did Andrew do after spending the day with Jesus? What did Jesus say to Andrew's brother? (John 1:35–42)

Who did Jesus call next to follow Him? Where was this man from? Who did Philip then find and what did he tell this person? What was Nathanael's reaction? (John 1:43–46)

Summarize the exchange between Jesus and Nathanael. Why did Nathanael proclaim that Jesus was the Son of God? How does Jesus respond to Nathanael's proclamation? (John 1:47–51)

Read John 2

What were the circumstances of Jesus' first miracle? What was the effect of this miracle on His disciples? (John 2:1–11)

What did Jesus find in the temple when He went up to Jerusalem for the Passover? What did Jesus do when He saw what was going on? What did He proclaim to those who were there? (John 2:12–16)

How did the Jews there respond to Jesus' actions in the temple courts? How did Jesus respond to them? What was Jesus doing in Jerusalem that caused many people to believe in Him? (John 2:18–24)

Read John 3

How was it that Nicodemus knew that Jesus was surely a teacher from God? Jesus mentions the kingdom of God two times in these verses; what truths from Jesus should we be aware of? (John 3:1–7)

Why did God send His Son? What are we told about those who do and those who do not believe in Jesus? Why do certain people refuse to come into the light? (John 3:16–20)

Summarize what John the Baptist said here about Jesus. What does John say about those who believe in Jesus? What does he say about those who reject Jesus? (John 3:31–36)

Saturday

Read John 4:1–26

At what town did Jesus meet the woman who had come out to draw water? What are we told of Jesus' condition at this time? What did Jesus ask the woman and how did she respond? (John 4:4–9)

What did Jesus tell the woman to do that opened the door for her past to be revealed? How did she respond to this command? What did Jesus tell her about her past? How did she respond to this? (John 4:16–19)

Summarize the things that Jesus says in response the woman's attempt to turn the confrontation of her past into a spiritual argument. What does Jesus say that makes it clear who He is? (John 4:20–26)

Week 2 — This week's Bible reading will continue our walk through the Gospel of John. We will look at the healing of the official's son, the healing of the paralyzed man, Jesus' authority to minister, and Jesus teaching at the Feast of Tabernacles.

Monday

Read John 4:27–54

What did Jesus consider His food? What did Jesus tell His disciples about the harvest among them? To what sort of crop was He referring? (John 4:34–36)

What happened in this Samaritan town because of Jesus' interaction with the woman at the well? After this event, who did the Samaritans believe Jesus to be? (John 4:39–42)

What was the setting of Jesus' healing of the royal official's son? How exactly did Jesus heal the official's boy? How did the official express faith in Jesus in this circumstance? (John 4:46–54)

Tuesday

Read John 5:1–18

What was the setting of this healing event? How many blind, lame and paralyzed were present at this place? What are we told about the man who Jesus singled out? (John 5:1–5)

What did Jesus do when He saw the man who had been lying there? How did the invalid reply to Jesus' inquiry? How exactly did Jesus heal the man? (John 5:6–9a)

What else are we told about the timing of this healing event? Why did this bring persecution against Jesus? How did Jesus respond to the Jews in verse 17? (John 5:9b–18)

Wednesday

Read John 5:19–45

What do we learn here about how Jesus operated in ministry? What do we learn about the relationship between Jesus and His Father? (John 5:19–20)

What do we learn about Jesus concerning His authority to judge men? What does He say about those who hear and believe in Him? What do we learn about the resurrection of the dead? (John 5:22–30)

What did Jesus say witnessed to His being sent by the Father? What warning can we take from verses 39–40? (John 5:36–40)

Read John 6

Why did the crowd follow Jesus to the far shore of the Sea of Galilee? How much food did the boy have that Andrew mentioned to Jesus? What exactly did Jesus do to perform this miracle? (John 6:1–13)

How did Jesus define the work of God? How did the Jews react to this? (John 6:29–31)

Who did Jesus say was the bread of God? How did the people react to this? What promises did Jesus give to those who come to Him? (John 6:33–35)

Read John 7

Why did Jesus purposefully stay away from Judea? Why did Jesus' brothers urge Him to go to Judea? What was Jesus' response to His brothers? (John 7:1–9)

When did Jesus go to the temple courts and begin teaching? What was the reaction of the crowd to His teaching? What did Jesus say about His teaching? (John 7:14–17)

What did Jesus proclaim on the last and greatest day of the feast? What are we told that this meant? (John 7:37–39)

Read John 8

Who did Jesus claim to be? What did he say about those who follow Him? (John 8:12)

What warning did Jesus give those listening? What can we learn from this? (John 8:24)

What did Jesus say about those who abide in His word? What promise did He give to those who are His disciples? (John 8:31–32)

Week 3 — This week's Bible reading will continue our walk through the Gospel of John. We'll cover the healing of the man born blind, Jesus the Good Shepherd, Jesus raising Lazarus, the triumphal entry, Jesus washing the disciple's feet, and Jesus as the Way.

Monday

Read John 9

What did Jesus' disciples ask Him concerning the man who was born blind? How did Jesus answer their question? How did Jesus heal the man? What did the blind man do? (John 9:1–7)

How did the man's neighbors respond to his healing? (John 9:8–9)

How did the Pharisees respond to the man's healing? (John 9:15–16, 28–29 & 34)

Read John 10

What does Jesus say about Himself in these verses? What does Jesus say about the hired hand? (John 10:7–13)

What does Jesus say about His sheep and what He gives His sheep? What does He tell us about His Father? (John 10:27–30)

Why were the Jews about to stone Jesus? How did Jesus defend His claims of being God's Son? (John 10:33–38)

Read John 11

How did Jesus find out about Lazarus' sickness? What did He do in response to this news? (John 11:1–6)

What was Lazarus' condition when Jesus arrived at Bethany? How did Martha respond to Jesus when she met Him? What did Jesus reveal about Himself in this exchange? (John 11:17–27)

How exactly did Jesus raise Lazarus from the dead? (John 11:38–44)

Read John 12

Why did a large crowd of Jews go to where Jesus was? What was one of the results of Lazarus being raised from the dead? (John 12:9–11)

How did Jesus enter Jerusalem? What was the reaction of those who came to meet Jesus? How did the Pharisees react to the people going out to meet Jesus? (John 12:12–19)

What does Jesus teach us about those who believe in Him? What does Jesus teach us about those who reject Him and do not accept His words? (John 12:44–50)

Read John 13

What did Jesus do in this passage? How did Peter react to this act of serving? Why did Jesus do this? (John 13:4–9 & 12–15)

What are we told about Jesus identifying the one who would betray him? What happened to this person? (John 13:21–30)

What was the new command that Jesus gave us? What did He say would be the results of us obeying this command? (John 13:34–35)

Read John 14

What did Jesus tell us to do in these verses? What information did He give us about the future place for those who trust in Him? What did Jesus say He would do? (John 14:1–3)

What did Jesus say about Himself in this verse? What does he say about the way to God? What else does Jesus reveal about God? (John 14:6–7)

What are we told about the ministry of the Holy Spirit? What name does Jesus use to describe Him? What promise does Jesus give us about having peace? (John 14:26–27)

Week 4 — This week's Bible reading will conclude our walk through the Gospel of John. We will look at Jesus as the vine, Jesus teaching about the Holy Spirit, Jesus praying, Jesus' arrest and crucifixion, and Jesus' resurrection and appearance to His disciples.

Monday

Read John 15

What do these verses say about our ability to bear fruit? (John 15:1–5)

What are we told is a key to remaining in God's love and having our joy be full? What does Jesus define as the greatest act of love for others? (John 15:9–13)

From these verses what are we told we should expect from the world? Why are we told we would be treated this way by the world? (John 15:18–21)

Read John 16

What does Jesus teach here about the Holy Spirit and His work in the world? (John 16:7–11)

What name does Jesus use for the Holy Spirit in this passage? What does Jesus say the Holy Spirit would do in our lives? (John 16:13–15)

Jesus uses the phrase "in that day" in verse 23. What day is He referring to? What does Jesus tell us about prayer in that day? (John 16:19–24)

Read John 17

Who was Jesus given authority over and by whom? How does Jesus define eternal life? (John 17:1–3)

What does Jesus pray for His disciples? What do we learn in verse 12? (John 17:11–12)

What does Jesus pray for those who would believe on Him through His disciple's message? Why does Jesus want those who believe in Him to be one? (John 17:20–23)

Read John 18

Who led the soldiers and officers to arrest Jesus? Who drew his sword and cut off the high priest's servant's ear? How did Jesus react to this? (John 18:2–11)

Who questioned Peter each time when he denied Christ? Where was Peter at these times? (John 18:15–18, 25–27)

Summarize Jesus' interaction with Pilate. What stands out to you in this conversation? (John 18:33–37)

Read John 19

How was Jesus treated by Pilate's soldiers? (John 19:1–3)

How did the chief priests and officers react when they saw Jesus in a crown of thorns and a purple robe? How did the Jews justify their call for Jesus' death? How did Pilate react to this? (John 19:5–11)

What are we told about Jesus' death that ensures to the reader that Jesus did in fact die? How did His death fulfill prophecy? (John 19:31–37)

Saturday

Read John 20–21

Who did Jesus first appear to after His death? Summarize this interaction. (John 20:11–18)

What are we told about other signs that Jesus did? Why were the miracles in this gospel selected? (John 20:30–31)

What miracle did Jesus perform that opened the disciple's eyes to who it was? How did Peter react to the realization that it was Jesus on shore? What happened when they landed? (John 21:4–14)

Week 5 — This week's Bible reading will begin our time in the book of Romans. We will be looking at the power of the gospel and man's condition, judgment and righteousness, justification by faith, the faith of Abraham, and rejoicing in hope and suffering.

Monday

Read Romans 1

What do we learn about the gospel in these verses? What do we learn about why men are without an excuse for believing? (Romans 1:16–20)

How are dishonorable passions defined in these verses? (Romans 1:26–27)

What are some characteristics of people who do not see fit to acknowledge God. (Romans 1:28–32)

Read Romans 2

Explain how we can condemn ourselves when judging another. What are we told about God's kindness? (Romans 2:1–4)

What are we taught here about God's judgment and reward? What are we specifically told about God and partiality? (Romans 2:6–11)

What do we learn here about inward circumcision versus an outward circumcision? (Romans 2:25–29)

Read Romans 3

What are we told about mankind's standing before God? (Romans 3:9–12)

What is God's remedy for mankind's condition? (Romans 3:21–24)

What does it say that God did to atone for our sins? How is mankind justified before God? (Romans 3:25–28)

Read Romans 4

What do we learn about faith and works as it relates to being made righteous before God? Who is considered Blessed? (Romans 4:4–8)

Under what circumstances was Abraham given the sign of circumcision? Who is he proclaimed to be the father of? (Romans 4:9–12)

How is Abraham's faith described? (Romans 4:18–22)

Read Romans 5

What benefit are we told comes with being justified by faith? What hope do we now have? (Romans 5:1–2)

What else are we told that we should rejoice in? Why are we told to do this? (Romans 5:3–5)

Contrast the results of what Adam did with what Christ did. (Romans 5:15–19)

Saturday

Read Romans 6

What are we told about baptism in these verses? What does it say about our being united with Christ in His death? What are we to no longer be? (Romans 6:3–7)

List out what we are told to do in these verses. (Romans 6:11–13)

What does this passage teach about sin and the free gift of God? (Romans 6:20–23)

Week 6 — This week's Bible reading will continue our time in the book of Romans. We will be looking at the law, sin and the body, Israel and the stumbling stone, the process of salvation, Israel and election, and living sacrifices.

Monday

Read Romans 7

How long does the law have authority over a person? What example is used to make this point? What specifically are we told about our old way and new way from verses 5–6? (Romans 7:1–6)

What is Paul attempting to convey to the reader when he talks about not doing what he wants to do? (Romans 7:15–20)

What law does Paul speak of in these verses? Who did Paul look to for rescue from the condition he described? (Romans 7:21–25)

Read Romans 8

Why is there now no condemnation for those who are in Christ? How did God accomplish this? (Romans 8:1–4)

How does Paul contrast life by the flesh and life by the Spirit? (Romans 8:5–8)

What are we told about things being able to separate us from the love of God? (Romans 8:35–39)

Read Romans 9

Why does Paul mention having sorrow and unceasing anguish of heart? What things does Paul say belong to the people of Israel? (Romans 9:1–5)

Who are regarded as Abraham's offspring? (Romans 9:7–8)

What was the "stumbling stone" over which Paul said that Israel had stumbled? (Romans 9:30–33)

Thursday

Read Romans 10

What was Israel's critical mistake concerning God's righteousness? What are we told about Christ, the law, and God's righteousness? (Romans 10:1–4)

How are we told salvation occurs in people? (Romans 10:9–12)

What is the progression Paul describes that enables people to be saved? Why is being sent by God so important to the process? (Romans 10:13–15)

Read Romans 11

What did Israel's trespass mean for the Gentiles and the world? What are we told Israel's rejection has meant? What will their acceptance mean? (Romans 11:11–15)

What very sobering thoughts are we given in these verses? What are we warned to do and not do? (Romans 11:17–21)

Why has Israel been partially hardened, and when will this end? What are we told about Israel in verse 28–29? (Romans 11:25–29)

Read Romans 12

What are we urged to do and why? (Romans 12:1–2)

Examine the list of spiritual gifts. How is each one specifically to be exercised? (Romans 12:6–8)

Look at the list of instruction in these verses. Which ones stand out and why? (Romans 12:9–21)

Week 7 — This week's Bible reading will conclude our time in the book of Romans. We'll also cover the book of Ruth. In Romans, we will look at the role of government, clean and unclean foods, and Paul's ministry. In Ruth, we'll look at an amazing story of God's grace.

Monday

Read Romans 13

Why are we told to submit to the governing authorities? What is mentioned about those who resist the established authority? What are we told about taxes? (Romans 13:1–7)

What are we to continue to owe? What are we told sums up all the commandments? Why is this so? (Romans 13:8–10)

What are we told to do in these verses? (Romans 13:12–14)

Read Romans 14

What are we told to do in these verses? (Romans 14:1–3)

What are we told about unclean food and how we should act around those who consider certain foods as unclean? How does Paul define the characteristics of the kingdom of God? (Romans 14:14–18)

What else are we told to do in these verses? (Romans 14:19–22)

Read Romans 15–16

What do we learn about the Scriptures in these verses? What blessing did Paul speak to the believers in Rome? (Romans 15:4–6)

Explain Paul's mission and ambition as relayed to us in these verses? (Romans 15:17–20)

What warning were the believers given in verse 17? What do we learn from Paul's final words to the believers in Rome? (Romans 16:17, 25–27)

Read Ruth 1

Why did Naomi and her family end up living in Moab? What happened to her family while in Moab? (Ruth 1:1–5)

How did Naomi try to persuade her daughters-in-law to stay in Moab? How did Orpah and Ruth each react to Naomi's urging? (Ruth 1:8–17)

How did the people of Bethlehem react to the arrival of Naomi and Ruth? How did Naomi explain her situation to the townspeople? (Ruth 1:19–21)

Read Ruth 2

What did Boaz say to Ruth? How did she respond? What did Boaz explain as his reason for showing favor to Ruth? (Ruth 2:8–11)

How else did Boaz show favor toward Ruth? (Ruth 2:14–16)

How did Naomi react to hearing where Ruth had gleaned that day? What else do we learn about Boaz? (Ruth 2:19–22)

Read Ruth 3–4

What did Naomi tell Ruth to do and why? What did Ruth do? (Ruth 3:1–6)

What happened in the middle of the night at the threshing floor? What issue had to be resolved before Boaz could redeem and take Ruth as his wife? (Ruth 3:8–13)

What did Boaz tell the kinsman-redeemer initially and how did this man initially react? What else did Boaz say that caused the kinsman-redeemer to give up his right to redeem? What do we learn in verse 17? (Ruth 4:3–6, 13, 17)

Week 8 — This week's Bible reading will begin a walk through the first twenty-four chapters of the book of Exodus. We'll look at the oppression of the Israelites in Egypt, the birth of Moses, Moses fleeing to Midian, the burning bush, and Moses' return to Egypt.

Monday

Read Exodus 1

What happened to the Israelites after Joseph and his generation died? What was the new king's attitude toward the Israelites? What reason did he present for oppressing the Israelites? (Exodus 1:6–10)

What happened to the Israelites as the oppression increased? How did the Egyptians react to this? (Exodus 1:11–14)

What did the king of Egypt command next? What did the Hebrew midwives do in response? How did God repay the midwives? (Exodus 1:15–21)

Tuesday

Read Exodus 2

How did Pharaoh's daughter find the baby Moses? How did Moses get his name? (Exodus 2:1–10)

Why did Moses flee from Egypt to Midian? (Exodus 2:11–15)

What happened to Moses after coming to Midian? (Exodus 2:16–22)

Wednesday

Read Exodus 3

What did God speak to Moses concerning the Israelites who were in Egypt? What do we learn about God's nature from this passage? What specifically did God tell Moses to do? (Exodus 3:7–10)

What was Moses' reaction to God's call on his life? How did God respond to Moses' reaction? (Exodus 3:11–12)

What did God tell Moses concerning the king of Egypt's response to his request to free the Israelites? What did God say about the Israelites' ultimate deliverance from Egypt? (Exodus 3:18–22)

Read Exodus 4

What three signs did God give Moses to perform before the people so that they would believe that God had appeared to him? (Exodus 4:1–9)

Why did the LORD's anger burn against Moses? What was God's solution to Moses' insecurity? (Exodus 4:10–16)

What happened when Aaron met Moses in the wilderness? What happened when Moses and Aaron met the elders of the Israelites? (Exodus 4:27–31)

Read Exodus 5

How did Pharaoh first react to Moses and Aaron's request to let the Israelites go? What was the ultimate result of this first encounter with Pharaoh? (Exodus 5:1–9)

How did the Israelite foremen react to the decision by Pharaoh? How did Pharaoh respond to their plea? How did the foremen speak to Moses and Aaron about their situation? (Exodus 5:15–21)

What did Moses do after being confronted by the Israelite foremen? (Exodus 5:22–23)

Saturday

Read Exodus 6

What specifically did God promise the Israelites that He would do? (Exodus 6:6–8)

Why did the Israelites react to these promises from the Lord the way they did? (Exodus 6:9)

What did God tell Moses to do and why did Moses balk at this command? (Exodus 6:10–12)

Week 9 — This week's Bible reading will continue our walk through the book of Exodus. We'll look at Moses and Aaron before Pharaoh, the plague of frogs, gnats, flies, livestock, hail, locusts, darkness, and the firstborn. We'll also look at the Passover and the Exodus.

Monday

Read Exodus 7

What did the LORD tell Moses and Aaron to do before Pharaoh? What happened as a result of this? (Exodus 7:8–13)

What things did God tell Moses to say to Pharaoh? (Exodus 7:15–18)

What happened when Aaron's staff struck the Nile? How did the magicians and Pharaoh respond to this? How did the Egyptians respond? (Exodus 7:20–24)

Tuesday

Read Exodus 8

What did Moses warn Pharaoh concerning? What are we told about what Pharaoh did after the frogs died? (Exodus 8:1–4, 12–15)

What are we told about the plague of gnats that differs from the previous plagues? What is similar to the prior plagues? (Exodus 8:16–19)

What was different about the plague of flies compared to the prior plagues? How did Pharaoh initially respond to this plague? How did Pharaoh respond after the flies had left? (Exodus 8:22–25, 30–32)

Read Exodus 9

What happened to the livestock of the Egyptians? What happened to the livestock of the Israelites? How did Pharaoh react to all this? (Exodus 9:1–7)

What do we learn about God's purpose in raising up Pharaoh? What warning was given to Pharaoh and his officials? How did they respond to this warning? (Exodus 9:16–21)

What happened when Moses stretched his staff out toward the sky? Where did it not hail? How did Pharaoh respond to this plague? (Exodus 9:23–28, 34–35)

Read Exodus 10

How did Pharaoh's officials react to the threat of the plague of locusts? What did Pharaoh say to Moses and Aaron? How did this conversation end? (Exodus 10:7–11)

What did Pharaoh do hastily after the locusts invaded the land? How did Moses respond to his plea? How did Pharaoh respond once the plague had passed? (Exodus 10:16–20)

What are we told about the plague of darkness? What qualification did Pharaoh put on the Israelites leaving to worship the LORD? How did this interaction between Moses and Pharaoh end? (Exodus 10:21–29)

Read Exodus 11

What were the specifics of this plague as spoken by Moses to Pharaoh? (Exodus 11:4–7)

What did God tell Moses to tell the people to do? How were the Israelites and Moses perceived by the Egyptians at this point? (Exodus 11:2–3)

What did Moses tell Pharaoh the results of this last plague would be? (Exodus 11:8)

Saturday

Read Exodus 12

What are some instructions the LORD give Moses and Aaron concerning how the Israelites were to keep the Passover? (Exodus 12:1–11)

How did Pharaoh and his people react to this final plague? What did the Israelites take with them out of Egypt? (Exodus 12:31–36)

What regulations were placed on participating in the Passover? (Exodus 12:43–49)

Week 10 — This week's Bible reading will continue our walk through the book of Exodus. We'll look at the Feast of Unleavened Bread, crossing the Red Sea, the Song of Moses, the waters of Marah, manna, water from a rock, and the defeat of the Amalekites.

Monday

Read Exodus 13

Why did Moses tell the people to remember this day? How were they supposed to commemorate what the LORD had done for them? What were they supposed to tell their sons about this? (Exodus 13:3–8)

What do we learn about the consecration of the firstborn? (Exodus 13:11–16)

Why did God lead the Israelites through the desert and not through the land of the Philistines? Why did Moses take the bones of Joseph with him? How did the LORD's presence go with the Israelites? (Exodus 13:17–22)

Tuesday

Read Exodus 14

What did Pharaoh and his servants say after the Israelites departed? What does this tell us about their motivation to take actions? What did they do? (Exodus 14:5–9)

How did the Israelites react to the approaching Egyptian army? How did Moses respond to the people? What did the LORD tell Moses to do? (Exodus 14:10–16)

What happened after the Israelites crossed through the Red Sea? How did the Israelites respond to all this? (Exodus 14:26–28, 31)

Read Exodus 15

What is the main theme of this song? What did Moses and the Israelites declare about the LORD? (Exodus 15:1–5)

What characteristics of the LORD are revealed to us in these verses? (Exodus 15:11–13)

What happened when the Israelites came to Desert of Shur? What did Moses do concerning the water? What did LORD decree to the people? (Exodus 15:22–26)

Read Exodus 16

What did the Israelites do after having come into the Desert of Sin? What instructions did the LORD give Moses for the people? (Exodus 16:1–5)

What happened that evening and the next morning? What did Moses tell the people to do? How did some respond to Moses' instructions and what were the results? (Exodus 16:13–16, 19–20)

What happened when the people saved the manna for the Sabbath day? What were the instructions for the Sabbath? (Exodus 16:23–30)

Read Exodus 17

Why did the Israelites quarrel with Moses? What did Moses do in response? (Exodus 17:1–4)

What did the LORD tell Moses to do? How did Moses respond to the LORD? How did this place get named? (Exodus 17:5–7)

Who did Moses send to meet the Amalekites in battle? What part did Moses, Aaron, and Hur play in the battle? What was the outcome of the battle? (Exodus 17:8–13)

Read Exodus 18

What difficulty did Moses' father-in-law perceive when he watched what Moses was doing? (Exodus 18:13–18)

How did Jethro, Moses' father-in-law, react to hearing about what the LORD did for Israel? (Exodus 18:9–12)

What role did Moses' father-in-law suggest for Moses? What solution did his father-in-law bring to the problem? What did he say the results would be? (Exodus 18:19–23)

Week 11 — This week's Bible reading will conclude our walk through the first twenty-four chapters of the book of Exodus. We will look at the Israelites at Mount Sinai, the Ten Commandments, laws about Hebrew servants, personal injuries, and property rights.

Monday

Read Exodus 19

What did the LORD tell Moses when He called to him from the mountain? What promises were given by God? (Exodus 19:3–6)

What did the LORD say He would do and why? (Exodus 19:9)

What was the scene at the mountain on the morning of the third day? How did the people react to this? What did Moses do and how did God respond? (Exodus 19:16–19)

Read Exodus 20

Examine the second commandment closely. What did God tell them not to do? What is revealed about God's nature from these verses? (Exodus 20:4–6)

Look at the commandment to honor your father and mother. What promise is given for keeping this commandment? How is the final commandment different from the first nine commandments? (Exodus 20:12–17)

What commandment did the LORD reiterate with the people after giving the people the Ten Commandments? What instructions did the LORD provide concerning the altar? (Exodus 20:22–26)

Read Exodus 21

What things do we learn about the treatment of Hebrew slaves? (Exodus 21:1–6)

What acts resulted in the death penalty? When was the death penalty not to be enforced? (Exodus 21:12–17)

How are the phrases "eye for eye" and "tooth for tooth" used in context? (Exodus 21:22–25)

Read Exodus 22

What do we learn about the protection of property and penalties for stealing? (Exodus 22:1–4)

Review the commands stated here. What did the LORD specifically say concerning taking advantage of widows and orphans? (Exodus 22:16–24)

What other commands are stated in these verses? What does verse 27 reveal about the LORD? (Exodus 22:25–27)

Read Exodus 23

Review the "shall not" items stated here. What do we learn about the treatment of the property of an enemy in verses 4–5? (Exodus 23:1–9)

What instructions are given concerning the land during the seventh year? What reason is stated for resting from labor on the seventh day? (Exodus 23:10–12)

What did the LORD tell the Israelites to do when they reached the land where He was sending them? What benefits would their obedience reap? (Exodus 23:24–26)

Read Exodus 24

What did Moses do to confirm the covenant between God and the people? (Exodus 24:4–8)

Who went up the mountain and saw the God of Israel? What are we told that God did not do to these leaders? (Exodus 24:9–11)

Why did Moses go up the mountain? What happened when Moses went up the mountain? How did this appear to the Israelites? (Exodus 24:12–18)

Week 12 — This week's Bible reading will begin our walk through the book of Hebrews. We will be looking at Jesus' position in the universe, His high-priesthood, Jesus and Moses, maturity and immaturity, and our hope.

Monday

Read Hebrews 1

List out what these verses tell us about Jesus, God's Son. (Hebrews 1:1–4)

What are some of the things we are told about Jesus and angels in the scriptures quoted in this passage? (Hebrews 1:5–9)

What else are we told about Jesus from this passage? What are we told about the future of the earth and the heavens? What else are we told about the role of angels? (Hebrews 1:10–14)

Tuesday

Read Hebrews 2

Why are we told to pay more careful attention to what we've heard? How was our salvation declared and attested? Who also bore witness to this and how? (Hebrews 2:1–4)

What do we learn about Jesus? What do these verses say He did for us? (Hebrews 2:5–9)

What are we told the death of Jesus accomplished? What kind of high priest is Jesus? Why is Jesus able to help us when we are tempted? (Hebrews 2:14–18)

Read Hebrews 3

What is said about us as believers in this passage? What are we encouraged to do? What are we told about Jesus and Moses from these verses? (Hebrews 3:1–6)

What are we warned about in this passage? What example is used here as a warning? (Hebrews 3:7–11)

What are we warned about in these verses? What are we told to do for one another, how often, and why? (Hebrews 3:12–13)

Thursday

Read Hebrews 4

To whom did the gospel have no benefit? What are we told about those who believed the gospel? What warning are we given in verse 7? (Hebrews 4:1–7)

What is said about the attributes of the word of God? What does it say God sees? What do we learn here about giving an account for our lives? (Hebrews 4:12–13)

What does this passage reveal about Jesus? What can we do confidently because of Jesus? (Hebrews 4:14–16)

Read Hebrews 5

What are we told about the role and characteristics of a high priest? How was Jesus made a high priest and in what order? (Hebrews 5:1–6)

What insights are we given into Jesus' prayer life? What is said about Jesus' obedience and His suffering and what this brought about? (Hebrews 5:7–10)

What are some of the characteristics of immature believers mentioned here? How are mature believers defined? (Hebrews 5:11–14)

Read Hebrews 6

What are the elementary doctrines mentioned here that are said to be foundational? (Hebrews 6:1–3)

What are we told about God and what He will do? What is said about how we show love to God? What are we encouraged to do in light of this? (Hebrews 6:10–12)

How are we told we might have strong encouragement? What is said to be an anchor for our souls? (Hebrews 6:17–20)

Week 13 — This week's Bible reading will conclude our walk through the book of Hebrews. We'll look at Melchizedek, Jesus as our high priest, the earthly tabernacle, the power of the blood of Christ, the law and Christ's sacrifice, and the heroes of the faith.

Monday

Read Hebrews 7

Who was Melchizedek and what did he do? (Hebrews 7:1–3, 6)

What is said about the power and longevity of Jesus' priesthood? What are we told about the former commandment and a better hope? (Hebrews 7:15–18)

What do we learn about Jesus and His ministry as a priest? (Hebrews 7:22–28)

Read Hebrews 8

What do we see concerning where Jesus is now and what He is doing? What are we told about the ministry of the high priest and the nature of Jesus' ministry? (Hebrews 8:1–6)

What are we told in this passage about the old and new covenants? (Hebrews 8:7–9)

What major elements are we told about concerning the new covenant? (Hebrews 8:10–13)

Read Hebrews 9

Who could enter the second section, the Most Holy Place of the tent, how often, and with what? What was the Holy Spirit indicating to us by this? (Hebrews 9:6–8)

What do we learn about what Jesus did and what He secured? What does the blood of Christ do for us and enable us to do? (Hebrews 9:11–14)

What are we told that Christ did and will do? (Hebrews 9:24–28)

Thursday

Read Hebrews 10

How does this passage describe the law, its ability to cleanse worshippers, and its ability take away sins? (Hebrews 10:1–4)

What is said in this passage about the power of Jesus' sacrifice? (Hebrews 10:8–14)

What are we encouraged to do in light of what Jesus has done for us? How can we put these instructions into practice? (Hebrews 10:19–25)

Read Hebrews 11

What things are we are told that Abraham did by faith? (Hebrews 11:8–9)

What do we learn about Moses from this passage and how he lived by faith? What did Moses consider of greater value than the treasures of Egypt and why? (Hebrews 11:23–28)

What are some things the saints of old did by faith? How were some of them mistreated? Why were they willing to be mistreated? (Hebrews 11:32–40)

Read Hebrews 12–13

What does this passage tell us about discipline. What are we specifically told concerning God's discipline? What are we told is the end result of discipline? (Hebrews 12:4–11)

Concerning our relationships with others, what are we told to do? What are we told to keep our lives free from and why? (Hebrews 13:1–5)

What are we told to do concerning our leaders? What warning is given to leaders? (Hebrews 13:7, 17, 24)

Weekly Memory Verses

Week 1 — John 3:18 — "Whoever believes in him is not condemned, but whoever does not believe is condemned already, because he has not believed in the name of the only Son of God." (ESV)

Week 2 — John 7:38 — "Whoever believes in me, as the Scripture has said, 'Out of his heart will flow rivers of living water.'" (ESV)

Week 3 — John 10:27–28 — "My sheep hear my voice, and I know them, and they follow me. I give them eternal life, and they will never perish, and no one will snatch them out of my hand." (ESV)

Week 4 — John 17:3 — "And this is eternal life, that they know you, the only true God, and Jesus Christ whom you have sent." (ESV)

Week 5 — Romans 6:23 — "For the wages of sin is death, but the free gift of God is eternal life in Christ Jesus our Lord." (ESV)

Week 6 — Romans 12:21 — "Do not be overcome by evil, but overcome evil with good." (ESV)

Week 7 — Ruth 2:12 — "The LORD repay you for what you have done, and a full reward be given you by the LORD, the God of Israel, under whose wings you have come to take refuge!" (ESV)

Week 8 — Exodus 1:12 — "But the more they were oppressed, the more they multiplied and the more they spread abroad. And the Egyptians were in dread of the people of Israel." (ESV)

Week 9 — Exodus 9:16 — "But for this purpose I have raised you up, to show you my power, so that my name may be proclaimed in all the earth." (ESV)

Week 10 — Exodus 15:13 — "You have led in your steadfast love the people whom you have redeemed; you have guided them by your strength to your holy abode." (ESV)

Week 11 — Exodus 20:12 — "Honor your father and your mother, that your days may be long in the land that the LORD your God is giving you." (ESV)

Week 12 — Hebrews 2:18 — "For because he himself has suffered when tempted, he is able to help those who are being tempted." (ESV)

Week 13 — Hebrews 9:14 — "how much more will the blood of Christ, who through the eternal Spirit offered himself without blemish to God, purify our conscience from dead works to serve the living God." (ESV)

Journal & Notes

Journal & Notes

Journal & Notes

Journal & Notes

Journal & Notes

Journal & Notes

Journal & Notes

Journal & Notes

Journal & Notes

Journal & Notes

Journal & Notes

Journal & Notes

Journal & Notes

Made in the USA
Las Vegas, NV
16 December 2023

82973639R00057